DOMINOES

Sherlock Holmes: The Reigate Puzzle

Sir Arthur Conan Doyle

T0355167

Series Editor: Nicole Irving

Text adaptation by Lesley Thompson

Illustrated by Petur Antonsson

Sir Arthur Conan Doyle (1859–1930), born in Edinburgh, Scotland, is best known as the creator of Sherlock Holmes. He started writing after working as a doctor, and soon became one of the world's best-known authors. *Sherlock Holmes: The Blue Diamond, The Emerald Crown, The Norwood Mystery, The Sign of Four, The Speckled Band, The Dying Detective,* and *The Top-Secret Plans* are also available as Dominoes. His adventure story *The Lost World* is also a Dominoes reader.

OXFORD
UNIVERSITY PRESS

OXFORD

UNIVERSITY PRESS

Great Clarendon Street, Oxford, OX2 6DP, United Kingdom

Oxford University Press is a department of the University of Oxford.
It furthers the University's objective of excellence in research, scholarship,
and education by publishing worldwide. Oxford is a registered trade
mark of Oxford University Press in the UK and in certain other countries

© Oxford University Press 2018

The moral rights of the author have been asserted

First published in Dominoes 2018

2022

10 9 8 7 6 5 4 3 2

No unauthorized photocopying

All rights reserved. No part of this publication may be reproduced,
stored in a retrieval system, or transmitted, in any form or by any means,
without the prior permission in writing of Oxford University Press, or as
expressly permitted by law, by licence or under terms agreed with the
appropriate reprographics rights organization. Enquiries concerning
reproduction outside the scope of the above should be sent to the ELT
Rights Department, Oxford University Press, at the address above

You must not circulate this work in any other form and you must
impose this same condition on any acquirer

Links to third party websites are provided by Oxford in good faith and
for information only. Oxford disclaims any responsibility for the materials
contained in any third party website referenced in this work

ISBN: 978 0 19 460745 2   Book
ISBN: 978 0 19 460744 5   Book and Audio Pack
Audio not available separately

Printed in China

This book is printed on paper from certified and well-managed sources

ACKNOWLEDGEMENTS

Illustrations by: Petur Antonsson/Shannon Associates.

The publisher would like to thank the following for permission to reproduce photographs: Oxford
University Press p.42 (fingerprint under magnifying glass/Meg007/Shutterstock),
p.43 (fingerprint pair/Andrey_Kuzmin); Shutterstock pp.42 (dna strand/adike), (typing
on laptop/justyle), (policeman questioning woman at police station/photographee.eu),
p.43 (Officer in interrogation room showing a knife as a murder evidence/astock).

Contents

BEFORE READING

1 Here are some people in *The Reigate Puzzle*. Complete the sentences with their names. Use a dictionary to help you.

Colonel Hayter

Sherlock Holmes

Doctor Watson

Mr Cunningham

Alec Cunningham

Mr Acton

Inspector Forrester

a .... is a rich old man.

b .... is an important police officer.

c .... is a young man.

d .... is a famous detective.

e .... is an old army officer.

f .... is the young man's father.

g .... is Holmes's best friend.

2 What do you think happens in the story? Write the names from Activity 1.

a .... lives near Reigate, England. He invites Holmes and Watson to his house.

b .... wants Holmes to have a holiday.

c .... is looking for thieves and a murderer.

d .... helps Forrester to find the murderers.

e .... helps his father with a crime.

f .... loses some things from his house.

g .... wants Mr Acton's money.

Chapter 1
The murder

It is April 1887, and Sherlock Holmes is in France with his friend, **Doctor** Watson. After three months in Europe, Holmes is tired and ill.

'You must stop your work here now,' Watson tells him. 'Our French friends can finish without you. We must go home to England, I think. You're not very well.'

Three days later, the two men are at Sherlock Holmes's house in Baker Street, in London. Holmes is no better.

'I know!' Watson thinks. 'Sherlock needs a **rest**. My old friend **Colonel** Hayter is always asking me to visit him at his home in the country. Sherlock can come with me and he can have a good rest there.'

Doctor (or **Dr**) this person helps people when they are ill

rest when you are quiet and do not work; to sit quietly and do nothing

colonel an important person in the army

pistol a small gun; a person can kill someone with this

thief (*plural* **thieves**) a person who takes things without asking

A week later, Holmes and Watson are at Colonel Hayter's house near Reigate. Hayter is a good man, and Holmes likes him.

On their first evening there, after they all finish eating, Holmes is resting in a big chair. Watson and Hayter are looking at the colonel's **pistols** – he has got many interesting ones from different countries.

Suddenly, Hayter says, 'Tonight, I'm taking one of these pistols to my bedroom with me.'

'Why?' Watson asks.

'Well, some **thieves** are working near here and I'm a little afraid,' Colonel Hayter says. 'Old Mr Acton, an

important man in the village, is very angry about it. The thieves have got some things from his house: an old book, a picture, two bottles, a clock, and some pens. Nothing important.'

'But why those things?' Watson says.

Holmes looks up from his chair.

'Hmm, yes, why? It's interesting to me. Those things are important **clues** for the **police**. I would like to know more about it.'

Watson speaks quickly. 'You're here for a rest, Holmes. Please don't begin working again!'

Holmes smiles, but he says nothing.

clue something that helps the police

police men and women who stop people doing bad things

3

servant a person who works for someone

murder the time when a murderer kills someone

shot this comes out of a gun

shoot to use a gun

The next morning, at breakfast, the colonel's **servant** comes quickly into the room.

'Colonel Hayter, I must tell you something bad!' he cries excitedly. 'It's at the Cunninghams' house!'

'What? Is it those thieves again?' the colonel asks.

'No, this time it's worse. It's **murder**!'

'Murder?' the colonel cries. 'Is it old Mr Cunningham or his son?'

'No, it isn't them,' the servant says. 'It's their servant, William.'

'William Kirwan is dead?' the colonel cries.

'Yes, from a pistol **shot**, Alec tells me,' answers the servant. 'William sees the thief when the thief is going through a door at the Cunninghams' house, so William goes nearer. He wants to stop the thief, but then the thief **shoots** William and kills him.'

'What time did this happen?' the colonel asks.

'Last night, Colonel, at about twelve o'clock.' The colonel's servant leaves the room.

READING CHECK

Choose the correct words to complete the sentences.

a Holmes is *bad / ill* and needs a rest.

b He goes to Colonel Hayter's *house / hotel* with Watson.

c Holmes *isn't / is* interested in the crime at Acton's house.

d Old Mr Acton is *angry / happy* with the thieves.

e The thieves take a *clock / coat* and other things from Acton's house.

f Colonel Hayter's servant tells him something *good / bad*.

g The Cunninghams' *servant / sister* is dead.

h William Kirwan dies at about *two / twelve* o'clock.

WORD WORK

1 Find new words from Chapter 1 to match the pictures.

a r est

b t _ _ _ _

c s _ _ _ _ _ _

d m _ _ _ _ _

e d _ _ _ _ _

f p _ _ _ _ _

2 **Use the words in the bottle in the correct form to complete the sentences.**

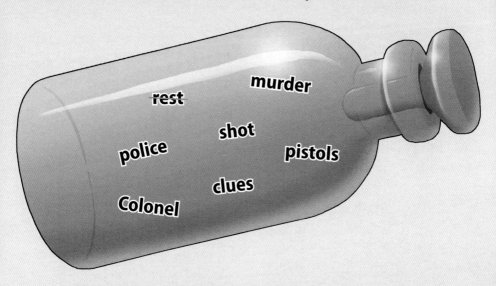

a Holmes needs to ....*rest*........ , but he loves working.

b Holmes and Watson visit .... Hayter's house.

c Hayter tells them about the .... at Acton's house.

d William Kirwan is dead from a pistol ....

e Colonel Hayter has many interesting .... from different countries.

f The .... are looking for the thieves.

g The thieves have got some of Acton's things from his house. These things are important .... , Holmes thinks.

GUESS WHAT

What happens in the next chapter? Tick (✔) one box to finish each sentence.

1 Holmes …
  a helps the police. ☐
  b kills Acton. ☐
  c writes a book. ☐

2 Colonel Hayter …
  a goes to London. ☐
  b talks about the Cunninghams. ☐
  c shoots Watson. ☐

Chapter 2
An important clue

coachman someone who drives a little car with horses

strange not usual

fight to talk angrily with someone; to hit someone again and again

lawyer someone who tells people the law (what they can or can't do)

Colonel Hayter looks at Holmes and Watson. 'This is very bad. William is the Cunninghams' **coachman** – and he's a good servant. Those thieves are murderers now.'

'This is a little **strange**,' Holmes says. 'Are the thieves staying in the village? Why don't they run away?'

The colonel says, 'Acton and Cunningham have got the biggest houses here and the thieves know that.'

'Do they have lots of money?' Watson asks.

'Yes, and they're **fighting** over it. The Cunninghams want half of old Mr Acton's money and their **lawyers** are fighting Mr Acton for it.'

The door opens and the servant says, '**Inspector** Forrester wants to see you, Colonel.'

A young man comes into the room.

'Good morning, Colonel Hayter,' he says. 'I have a question. Is Mr Holmes of Baker Street here?'

Holmes looks at the young man.

'Please can you come with me and look at the **scene** of the **crime**, Mr Holmes?'

Holmes laughs. 'You see, Watson? I can't rest. I must always work! Perhaps you can tell me a little more, Inspector.'

'Well, **sir**,' says Inspector Forrester, 'there's only one man, we think. The thief is the murderer, too. Old Mr Cunningham sees the murderer from his bedroom window. Alec, his son, sees him from **upstairs**, too. This happens at a quarter to twelve. Suddenly, they hear their coachman, William – he's crying for help. Alec runs **downstairs**. The back door is open and he sees two men fighting.

inspector an important person in the police

scene where something happens

crime killing someone, taking money from someone, or doing something very bad are all crimes

sir you say this when you talk to an important man

upstairs the upper part of a house

downstairs the lower part of a house

'One man shoots a pistol, the second man **falls** down, and the murderer runs across the garden and gets out through the **hedge**. Mr Cunningham, from his bedroom window, can see the man near the road, but only for a second. Alec stops and helps William. The murderer is not very tall and he's wearing a dark coat.'

'Does William say something before he dies?' Holmes asks.

'Not a word. William lives near the big house with his mother. He's a good servant. Perhaps, after the Acton crime, he thinks, "Where is the thief?". He wants to look at the big house before it gets dark. He finds the thief at the door, we think, and the thief shoots him.'

'What does his mother say about all of this?'

'She's very old and, of course, she's not thinking well after her son's murder. She knows nothing. But we have got something very important, and perhaps it can help us. Look!'

The inspector takes something from his **pocket** and gives it to Holmes. It is a little **piece** of **paper**.

fall (down) to go down suddenly

hedge a line of little trees in a garden

pocket the place in your coat where you can put things

piece not all of something

paper you can write on this

11

READING CHECK

Are these sentences true or false? Tick (✔) the boxes.   True   False

a The Cunninghams want half of old Mr Acton's money.   ✔   ☐
b Inspector Forrester wants Holmes's help.   ☐   ☐
c Alec and his father see the murderer, they say.   ☐   ☐
d The murderer runs into the house.   ☐   ☐
e The murderer is not very tall and he's wearing a dark hat.   ☐   ☐
f William's mother knows a lot about the crime.   ☐   ☐
g Inspector Forrester gives Holmes something.   ☐   ☐

WORD WORK

1 Unscramble the new words in the box from Chapter 2 and match them to the correct pictures.

| wonstrisad | ~~enees~~ | cropensit | edgeh | coptek | tighf | uatissrp | yerwal | reppa | lalf |

a crime scene   b ....   c ....   d ....   e ....

f ....   g ....   h ....   i ....   j ....

2 Complete the sentences with the words from Activity 1.

a The police are at the ....._scene_..... of the crime.

b I have some flowers and a .... in my garden.

c In a house, people usually eat ....

d Her son is an .... with the police.

e Be careful! It is very dark. Don't ....!

f Write your name on this piece of ....

g The bedrooms are usually .... in a house.

h Put the pen in your ....

i She is an important .... in London.

j People often .... about money.

GUESS WHAT

What happens in the next chapter? Tick (✔) two boxes.

a ☐ Holmes reads the piece of paper.

b ☐ Watson hits Colonel Hayter.

c ☐ Holmes goes to the Cunninghams' house.

d ☐ The inspector kills Mr Cunningham.

Chapter 3
The scene of the crime

'This is from the dead man's hand,' the inspector says. 'The time on it is the time of his death. Perhaps the murderer takes the piece of paper from William's hand when they fight, or perhaps William takes it from the murderer. Look.'

Holmes takes the paper from the inspector and looks at it carefully.

'What do you think, sir?' the inspector asks Holmes. 'Perhaps William Kirwan is working with the thief. They meet and William helps the man to get into the house. And then something goes wrong and they begin fighting.'

door

twelve

a surprise.

about this.

Holmes looks more carefully at the paper.

'Hmm. This **handwriting** is very interesting.' He thinks for a minute then says, 'I want to look more carefully at this crime. Watson, Colonel, please excuse me. I'm leaving you for now. Give me half an hour with the inspector.'

An hour and a half later, the inspector comes back without Holmes.

'Mr Holmes is waiting for us **outside**. We must all go to the Cunninghams' house', he says. 'He is very excited. Is he well, Doctor?' the inspector asks Watson.

'I don't know ... ' says Watson, 'but we can't stop him. He loves working!'

handwriting when someone writes with a pen, you see this

outside not in the house

The three men find Holmes outside. He is walking slowly and thinking.

'Hello, my friends. What an interesting morning! Here's the story up to now. We have William dead from a pistol shot. The murderer runs away through the hedge, Mr Cunningham and his son say. William's mother can't tell us very much. The inspector and I **agree**: the piece of paper in William's hand is very important. Now, there are two big questions. First, who is the writer of the words on the piece of paper? Second, where is **the rest** of the paper? Someone wants this paper a lot. Perhaps they take it, put it in their pocket, and don't see the piece in William's hand. The writer doesn't give the paper to William. Perhaps a different person gives it to him. Or perhaps it comes by **post**.'

'Yes, that's it!' the inspector cries. 'I know the postman well, and he tells me everything! William Kirwan and his mother never get **letters**, but yesterday there's one for William.'

'Very good!' Holmes says. 'I love working with you, Inspector!'

The men are walking past William's little house. They walk through the trees to the Cunninghams' big, old house. A policeman is standing next to the **kitchen** door.

agree to say what other people are saying; say 'yes'

the rest some, but not all, of something

post to send a letter to someone; you can use this to send a letter

letter a piece of paper with writing on it; you send it to someone

kitchen the room in a house where people make things to eat

towards nearer

terrible very bad

ground you walk on this outside

'Open the door, please,' Holmes says. 'This is the scene here last night, my friends. Old Mr Cunningham is at the window upstairs and he sees the murderer running away. Alec runs downstairs and goes **towards** William.' Suddenly Holmes stops talking.

Just then, two men come through the trees towards the house. One is old with white hair and dark eyes. The second man is younger. He smiles when he sees Holmes and his friends.

'What are you doing here?' the old man asks Holmes. 'You Londoners usually work more quickly than this!'

'Ah, you must give us more time,' Holmes says, with a smile.

'More time?' the young man says. 'Yes, I can understand that. You haven't got any clues at all!'

'That's not true,' the inspector says. 'We have got one clue. You see – oh, Mr Holmes, what's the matter?'

Something **terrible** is happening to Holmes. His eyes are dark in his white face and a terrible noise is coming from his mouth. He falls down onto the **ground** and his friends watch, afraid. What is the matter with him?

ACTIVITIES

READING CHECK

Put these sentences in the correct order. Number them 1–8.

a ☐ The inspector comes back without Holmes.

b ☐ The Cunninghams arrive through the trees.

c ☐ Holmes suddenly falls down.

d ☐ Holmes looks at the piece of paper carefully.

e ☐ Old Cunningham and Alec speak to Holmes.

f ☐ Holmes and the inspector leave Watson and Hayter.

g ☐ The inspector, Watson, and Hayter go to the Cunninghams' house with Holmes.

h ☐ Outside the kitchen door, Holmes talks about the night of the murder.

WORD WORK

1 Find new words or phrases from Chapter 3 in the hedge.

agreeoutsideletterhandwritingposttowardskitchengroundterribletherest

2 Complete the sentences with the correct form of the words from Activity 1.

a We always ..... *agree* ..... about the important things.

b Children, it's sunny. Go .... and play.

c His .... is very bad. Nobody can read it.

d John is in the .... He's making breakfast.

e This .... is very long. I can't read it now.

f Give me half the money now and .... later.

g Please put this letter in the .... for me.

h Quiet! Somebody is coming .... us. Look, it's our teacher!

i Look at me. Don't look down at the ....

j Murder is a .... crime.

GUESS WHAT

What happens in the next chapter? Choose the words to complete the sentences.

a Holmes feels *worse* / *better*.

b The Cunninghams *ask* / *answer* some questions.

c Mr Cunningham writes a *name* / *number* on a piece of paper.

d Holmes looks carefully at the Cunninghams' kitchen *cat* / *door*.

e Holmes wants to look at the Cunninghams' *house* / *garden*.

Chapter 4
In the Cunninghams' house

Watson and the colonel help Holmes into the kitchen and put him onto a big chair. For some minutes, he can't speak. Finally, he opens his eyes.

'I'm sorry,' he says. 'I am not very well and these things can happen very suddenly.'

'Do you want to go home? Alec can take you,' old Cunningham says.

'Thank you. That's good of you. But first I would like to ask you a question.'

'Of course. What is it?'

'I'm thinking about William again. Perhaps he arrives after his murderer goes into the house and not before. You are saying something different – that the thief never goes into the house. He's never in the house, and the door is open.'

'That's right,' old Cunningham says. 'Alec can hear very well but he hears nothing. There's no noise and there's nobody in the house.'

'Where are you sitting at that time, Alec?'

'In my bedroom,' the young man answers.

'Which window is that?'

'It's the last window on the left, next to my father's.'

'Are the **lights** on in the two rooms?'

'Yes, of course.'

'Isn't it a little strange?' asks Holmes. 'The thief wants to come into the house, but the lights are on and there are people in the house.'

'Well, yes, it's strange,' says Alec. 'And we need your help to understand it, Mr Holmes. But remember this: we have all of our things. The thief takes nothing.'

'Are you **sure**?' Holmes asks. 'This thief is very strange. Remember the clock, bottles, and pens from Acton's house.'

'We need your help, Holmes,' says old Cunningham. 'What can we do?'

'You must give a **reward** and you must do it quickly. Fifty **pounds** is good, I think. Look, I have the paper about the reward ready here.' Holmes takes it out of his pocket. 'Can you **sign** it, please?'

'Yes, of course,' says old Cunningham. He takes the paper and then he suddenly stops. 'This is not right, Holmes. It says the murder happens "at a quarter to one", not "a quarter to twelve".'

'Oh, I'm sorry,' says Holmes. 'I'm not often wrong, but I'm not thinking very well. Please can you **correct** the time for me?'

light a thing that helps you to see in the dark

sure when you feel something is true

reward money that you give to someone when they find something for you

pound money that you use in the UK

sign to write your name on something

correct to make something right

'Yes, of course.' Mr Cunningham writes on the paper and gives it back to Holmes. Holmes puts the paper carefully into his pocket.

'Now I think we must look at your house.'

Before he goes from the kitchen, Holmes looks carefully at the kitchen door. 'There are **marks** from something here,' he says, and then he asks, 'Don't you have **bars** on your doors, Mr Cunningham?'

'We don't usually need them,' old Cunningham answers.

'When do the servants go to bed?' asks Holmes.

'About ten o'clock.'

'William, your coachman, too?'

'Yes.'

'But that evening, at ten, William is not in bed,' says Holmes. 'I see. Now let us look at the house.'

mark something dirty, or of a different colour, that you see on something

bar a long, thick, flat piece of metal or wood

READING CHECK

Choose the best answer for each question.

a Why does Holmes go into the kitchen?
1 He needs to sit down.
2 He is hungry.
3 He sees the thief.

b Holmes's first question is about …
1 the garden.
2 William.
3 the piece of paper.

c Why are the lights on in the Cunninghams' house on the night of the murder?
1 The Cunninghams are in the house.
2 The thieves are in the house.
3 William is in the kitchen.

d What does Alec say about the thieves?
1 They have a lot of his things.
2 They know his father.
3 They do not come into the house.

e What does Holmes give to Mr Cunningham in the kitchen?
1 A book.
2 Some money.
3 Some paper with handwriting on it.

f What does Mr Cunningham write?
1 His name.
2 The number twelve.
3 The number one.

WORD WORK

Choose the correct new words from Chapter 4 to complete the sentences.
Use the pictures to help you.

a I need 20 *pounds* / *pens* to buy some new shoes.

b Please *finish* / *correct* this word. It's wrong on this piece of paper.

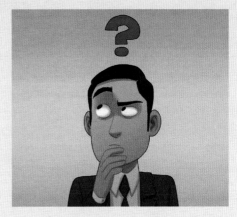

c There is a *reward* / *room* for information about the thief.

d Are you *sure* / *angry* about your answer? Perhaps you must think again.

e Look at the window! There is a *clock* / *light* on in the bedroom!

f Please *sign* / *smile* your name here. Then I will give you the money.

GUESS WHAT

What happens in the next chapter? Tick (✔) two boxes.

a ☐ Holmes finds the rest of the piece of paper.

b ☐ Holmes is angry when Watson knocks over a clue.

c ☐ Colonel Hayter shoots his pistol.

d ☐ The Cunninghams try to kill Holmes.

Chapter 5
The arrest

arrest the time
when the police
take someone to
prison; to take
someone to
prison

Holmes walks slowly, and he looks carefully at all the rooms in the house.

When they go upstairs, Mr Cunningham says, 'Mr Holmes, do we need to do all this? You can see, this is my bedroom and my son's bedroom is next to it.'

'I would like to see the garden from the bedrooms,' Holmes says. He walks to the window of Alec's room. 'Thank you. Now I'd like to see from the window in your room, Mr Cunningham.'

Everyone goes into old Cunningham's room, but Holmes and Watson go in last. Near the bed, there is a **bowl** of apples and a bottle of water on a little table. When he walks past, Holmes suddenly hits the table with his foot and everything falls on the **floor**. The apples go all over the room.

'Hey, Watson, be more careful!' Holmes cries.

Watson looks at Holmes in **surprise**, but he says nothing. He begins to get the apples, and the inspector and Colonel Hayter help him.

'But look,' the inspector says. 'Where is Holmes now? Why isn't he here?'

'Wait here,' Alec says. 'That Holmes man is **mad**. Come on, Father. Let's go and look for him.'

The Cunninghams leave. The inspector, the colonel, and Watson stay in the room.

'Alec is right,' the inspector says. 'Mr Holmes is a little mad, I'm afraid. Or perhaps he is ill again.'

Suddenly there is a terrible cry.

'Aargh! Help! Help! Murder!'

The cry comes from Alec's bedroom. Watson runs into the room with the other men behind him. There, he sees Sherlock Holmes on the floor. Alec has his hands

bowl a round container

floor the place in a room where you stand and walk

surprise something happening that you do not think of

mad not thinking right

27

around Holmes's **neck**. Old Cunningham is **pulling** one of Holmes's hands. Watson, the inspector, and the colonel pull the Cunninghams away and Holmes gets up. His face is white.

around all the way round

neck this is between your head and your body

pull to move something nearer you

'Arrest these men. They are the murderers of their coachman, William Kirwan.'

'Are you sure, Mr Holmes?' asks the inspector.

'Yes, I am. Look at their faces!' says Holmes.

At that moment, Alec takes a pistol from his pocket and gets ready to shoot. But before he can do this, the inspector hits Alec's arm and the pistol falls to the floor. The inspector calls for help and two policemen come into the room. They arrest the Cunninghams and take them away.

Holmes puts his foot on the pistol. 'We need this,' he says quietly. 'But we need *this* more.' He opens his hand – there is a piece of paper in it.

'The rest of the paper!' Watson cries.

'That's right. I can tell you everything later. First, I must go with the inspector and talk to the Cunninghams. Give me an hour.'

READING CHECK

Correct the sentences.

a Holmes wants to look at the garden from the ~~kitchen~~. *bedroom*

b There are some pens and water on the table in old Cunningham's bedroom.

c Holmes hits the table with his head.

d The Cunninghams look for Mr Acton.

e Holmes cries, 'Help! Help! Thief!'

f Alec tries to help Holmes.

g The inspector hits Alec's paper out of his hand.

h Now Holmes has the piece of bread in his hand.

WORD WORK

1 Complete the sentences on page 31 with words from the bedroom.

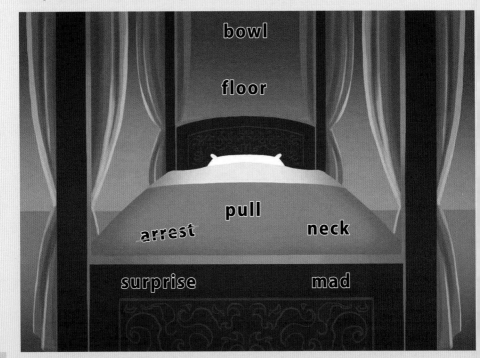

bowl

floor

pull

arrest   neck

surprise   mad

1 He wants to kill me. He's ....!

2 .....Arrest..... that thief now!

3 You are coming to see us tomorrow? What a nice ....!

4 Put some milk in .... a for the cat.

5 The boy can't swim. We must .... him out of the water.

6 Her bag is on the .... under the table.

7 The murderer has his hands around the man's ....

2 Now use the words from Activity 1 to complete the crossword.

GUESS WHAT

What happens in the next chapter? Tick (✔) the boxes.   Yes   No

a Holmes tells his friends all about the crime.   ☐   ☐

b Colonel Hayter sees the handwriting on the paper.   ☐   ☐

c Watson is angry with Holmes.   ☐   ☐

d Alec kills his father.   ☐   ☐

e Mr Acton finds his book, picture, bottles, clock, and pens. ☐   ☐

f Holmes feels better and goes back to Baker Street.   ☐   ☐

Chapter 6

The puzzle

At one o'clock, Holmes is back in the colonel's house with
Watson and Colonel Hayter. Mr Acton is there, too.

Holmes begins to speak.

'So, here's the **puzzle**. I'm very interested in the piece of
paper in William's hand. The murderer runs away after he
kills William, Alec says. So, the murderer doesn't have time
to take all of this piece of paper with him. Old Cunningham
comes downstairs after Alec, and he stays in the kitchen
with the servants, he says. Old Cunningham doesn't take
the paper. So, Alec takes the paper, I think. Now, let's look
again at the paper. What can we say about it?'

puzzle a picture
in many pieces
that you must
put together

'The handwriting is very strange,' the colonel says.

'Yes, it is,' Holmes says. 'It's strange because two people are writing this. One has a **strong** hand. The other has a **weaker** hand. Look at this word, and then look at this word here. They are very different.'

'It's true!' the colonel cries. 'But why do two people write it?'

'The two men are working on a terrible crime and one of them does not **trust** his "friend". Look carefully. The man with the stronger hand writes first, but he doesn't write all the words. He leaves **gaps** for the second man. These gaps are sometimes not very big, and the second man must write smaller. Perhaps the first man is more important in this crime.'

'Very good!' Mr Acton cries.

'There's more, and this is important. We can tell a man's age from his handwriting. The stronger writer is a young man. The weaker writer is older. These two pieces of handwriting are by men from one family, too. Look at the "e". And there are many more clues like this.'

'Now, William's body has a pistol shot, but there are no black marks on his coat. So the murderer shoots him from about four metres away. The two men are not fighting when the Cunninghams hear the shot. Why does Alec say he saw them fighting?'.

door
twelve
a surprise.
about this.

strong something that works well

weak not strong

trust to think that someone is nice and good

gap where there is nothing

truth something that is true or right

'The murderer runs away through the hedge, the Cunninghams say, too. But near the hedge, there's a little water on the ground ... the murderer runs through this water, so why are there no marks on the ground there? The Cunninghams are not telling the **truth** about the murderer.'

'Perhaps the Cunninghams are the murderers? And if Alec and old Mr Cunningham are the murderers, perhaps they are the thieves, too. And now, the question is this. Why do they go into Mr Acton's house? Do they need something for their lawyers in their fight against Mr Acton – some piece of paper, perhaps?'

'Ah, yes! ' Acton says. 'But they find nothing, because all my important papers are with my lawyer!'

'Yes,' says Holmes, and he smiles. 'They find no papers, so they take three or four things, but nothing important.'

'The inspector finds the little piece of paper in dead

William's hand. Now, we must ask, where is the rest of the paper, the bigger piece? Alec takes the paper from William, I think, but he leaves some of it in William's hand. Where does he put the bigger piece? That evening, he's wearing a **dressing gown**, so perhaps he puts the paper in his pocket. We go to the Cunninghams' house with the inspector. The Cunninghams aren't thinking about the paper at that time, but the inspector begins to tell them about it! Suddenly – what a surprise – I get ill and fall down!'

'What? You aren't ill?' the colonel cries, laughing. 'What a good **actor** you are, Holmes!'

'Yes,' says Holmes, 'and then, suddenly, I'm better again and I ask old Cunningham to "correct" the time on my paper with the reward on it. I want to see "twelve" in his handwriting. "Twelve" is when the murder happens and "twelve" is also written on the piece of paper from William's hand.'

dressing gown a coat that you wear at night in the house

actor someone who is in a film

'Then, in Alec's bedroom, I see his dressing gown on the back of the door. So when we visit old Cunningham's room, I hit the table with the bowl of apples on it and everybody comes to help. I quickly go back and look in the pockets of Alec's dressing gown. The paper's there. I take it – but suddenly, the Cunninghams are there and they have their hands on me. Alec nearly kills me, and old Cunningham pulls the paper from my hand – or he wants to. They are the criminals!'

'Later, after the arrest, I talk to old Cunningham about the murder. He tells me this: on the night of the crime at Acton's house, William goes after the Cunninghams and watches them. He then asks for money: "Give me the money," he says, "or I'm going to the police." So now Alec is very angry, and he wants to kill William. William gets a letter in the post and comes to the big house that night. Alec shoots him and takes the letter from his hand. But he does not get all of the letter. Here it is.'

Holmes puts the letter – the two pieces of paper – down on the table.

> Come to the kitchen door
> at a quarter to twelve
> and learn of a surprise.
> Say nothing about this.

'I don't know all of the story,' Holmes says. 'But we have the criminals and that's the important thing. Watson, I feel much better after my rest. We can go back to Baker Street tomorrow.'

Come to the kitchen door
at a quarter to twelve
and learn of a surprise.
Say nothing about this.

READING CHECK

Are these sentences true or false? Tick (✔) the boxes.

		True	False
a	William wants money from the Cunninghams.	✔	☐
b	Mr Acton is a thief.	☐	☐
c	Alec kills William.	☐	☐
d	The handwriting on the letter is from two different people.	☐	☐
e	The Cunninghams are thieves.	☐	☐
f	Alec takes all of the paper from William's hand.	☐	☐
g	Holmes finds some paper in Alec's dressing-gown pocket.	☐	☐
h	Holmes is a terrible actor.	☐	☐

WORD WORK

Complete the sentences with the new words from Chapter 6 in the picture of Mr Acton.

a Are you a thief? Tell me the ......truth......!

b His handwriting is very .... I think he is ill.

c It's very hot tonight. I don't need my ....

d Why is there a big .... between these two words?

e I don't .... that woman. She's bad.

f My uncle is an .... in films in Hollywood.

g You're .... Please can you help me with this big bag?

h Help me put this .... together. There are lots of pieces.

GUESS WHAT

What happens to Holmes after the story finishes?
Tick (✔) the boxes and add your own ideas.

a Holmes is ill again and goes to Europe. ☐

b He goes on holiday with Watson and there is another murder. ☐

c He is a famous actor in London. ☐

d Holmes writes a book about his work. ☐

e ....

f ....

PROJECT A *Interviewing a character*

1 Complete the police interview with Mr Acton. Put the policeman's questions in the correct order.

Are they murderers, do you think?

Why are your lawyers fighting them?

~~Where do you live, Mr Acton?~~

Do you know the Cunninghams?

What do you think of them?

How old are you?

Policeman: Good morning, Mr Acton. I have some questions for you.

Mr Acton: Of course.

Policeman: a) Where do you live, Mr Acton?

Mr Acton: Near Reigate.

Policeman: b)

Mr Acton: I'm sixty-four.

Policeman: c)

Mr Acton: Yes, but we aren't friends.

Policeman: d)

Mr Acton: I don't like them very much. They're always talking about money.

Policeman: e)

Mr Acton: Because they want more money – my money!

Policeman: f)

Mr Acton: I don't know, but they aren't very nice people.

2 Complete the interview with Colonel Hayter. Write answers to the policeman's questions. Use Activity 1 to help you.

near Reigate

58 years old

knows Acton – better than the Cunninghams

likes Acton – not sure about the Cunninghams

they have lots of money – but the Cunninghams want to have more

doesn't want to say

Policeman: Good morning. Do you live in London, Colonel Hayter?

Hayter: a) ....

Policeman: How old are you?

Hayter: b) ....

Policeman: Do you know Mr Acton and the Cunninghams well?

Hayter: c) ....

Policeman: Do you like them?

Hayter: d) ....

Policeman: Why are Mr Acton and the Cunninghams fighting, do you think?

Hayter: e) ....

Policeman: Are the Cunninghams murderers, do you think, Colonel Hayter?

Hayter: f) ....

3 Write six questions for an interview with Sherlock Holmes and one of the characters in this story.

4 Now write answers to Holmes's questions for your character in Activity 3.

5 Then work in pairs. Role-play the interview.

PROJECT B   *Solving crimes*

1 Sherlock Holmes is a detective. He looks for clues and solves crimes – he uses the clues to understand who is the thief or murderer. Police detectives solve crimes in different ways. Below are four different ways to solve crimes. Match the photos with the definitions. Use a dictionary to help you.

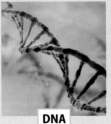   

| DNA | Digital footprint | Interview | Fingerprints |

a Everyone has this. It can be found in parts of your body like your hair. Nobody has yours.

....

b This is when the police or a detective asks someone questions.

....

c We leave this when we go online.

....

d A person without gloves on his or her hands can leave these.

....

2 Read about how a detective uses interviews to solve crimes. Then complete the notes on page 43.

When detectives think a person is a thief or a murderer, that person is a suspect. Detectives often talk to suspects in a crime. They ask the suspects questions, and write the answers. They often record the interview, too.

Sometimes a suspect's body can give clues – this is called 'body language'. Detectives look at the suspect's body language. They look at the suspect's face. Does he or she look happy or sad? Is he or she moving a lot? Perhaps he or she is afraid?

Detectives sometimes ask a question again later. Perhaps the suspect answers in a different way. Detectives listen to the recording after the interview, and think about any strange answers.

Way to solve crime: Interview

What is it? Detectives ask questions to **a)** ...*suspects*... in a crime.

What do detectives do? They:

- ask the suspect **b)** ....
- write the **c)** ....
- look at the suspect's **d)** .... language.
- sometimes ask a question again **e)** ....
- listen to the recording again **f)** ....
- think about any **g)** .... answers.

What does the suspect do?

- He or she **h)** .... the detective's questions.
- Perhaps he or she looks happy or **i)** ....
- Sometimes he or she moves a lot. Perhaps he or she is **j)** ....
- Perhaps he or she answers a question in a **k)** .... way or he or she says a
  l) .... answer.

**3 Complete the notes on how detectives use fingerprints to solve crimes, using the
words in the box.**

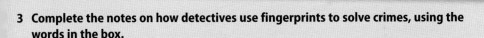

| criminal   detectives   fingerprints   marks   nothing   scene   windows |

Way to solve crime: a) Fingerprints

What is it? Looking at **b)** .... the criminal makes at the scene of a crime.

What does the criminal do? Perhaps the criminal has **c)** .... on his or her hands.
He or she leaves prints for **d)** .... to find.

What do detectives do?

- look for marks on doors, **e)** .... , tables, and chairs
- take a picture of the marks
- look at other fingerprints on the police computer.
  Are the fingerprints at the **f)** .... of a crime different?
  Perhaps they have a name with the fingerprints on the computer.
  Now they know the name of the **g)** ....

4 **Read the texts about two other ways police solve crimes. Choose the best words to complete the sentences.**

Every part of a person's body has **a)** DNA / Digital footprints in it. **b)** Everybody / Nobody has your DNA. Perhaps detectives find a hair at the scene of crime. They can look at the DNA in the hair and they can look at the DNA on the police computer.

Perhaps they have the **c)** criminal's / detective's DNA on the police computer. Now they know the **d)** age / name of the criminal.

A criminal sometimes leaves a digital **e)** fingerprint / footprint on a computer. The **f)** detective / suspect can learn about someone from his or her emails, or from what he or she looks at online. The detective will look for **g)** clues / papers on a suspect's computer and mobile **h)** phone / car.

5 **Look at four more ways of solving a crime. The words don't match the pictures. Correct them.**

~~phone position tracking~~
footprints

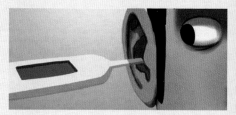

blood analysis

body temperature

footprints

6 **Choose one of the ways to solve a crime from Activity 5. Find out about it. Make notes and then write a paragraph about it. Use your notes and the texts in Activities 1–4 to help you.**

GRAMMAR CHECK

Present Simple: *Yes/No* questions and short answers

Yes/No questions start with the verb be, or an auxiliary verb, like do or can.

Are you sure? Yes, I am.

In the short answer, we reuse be or the auxiliary verb.

Do you want to go home? No, I don't (do not).

1 Write answers for the questions about Sherlock Holmes and *The Reigate Puzzle*. Use the short answers in the box.

> Yes, it is.   Yes, it's them.   Yes, I can.   No, she can't.   No, he isn't.
> ~~Yes, he is.~~   Yes, he does.   Yes, he is.   No, he doesn't.   Yes, he does.   Yes, he is.

a Is Sherlock Holmes tired after three months in Europe? ....Yes, he is.......

b Is Holmes better in his house in Baker Street? ....

c Does Holmes need a rest? ....

d Is Colonel Hayter a good man? ....

e Is William Kirwan dead? ....

f 'Please, can you look at the scene of the crime, Mr Holmes?' ....

g Does William say something before he dies? ....

h Can William's mother tell them something interesting? ....

i Does Holmes want to look at this crime more carefully? ....

j Is it murder at the Cunninghams' house? ....

k Are old Mr Cunningham and his son the the murderers? ....

GRAMMAR CHECK

Information questions and question words

We use question words in information questions. We answer these questions by giving some information.

What can we do?	*You must give a reward of fifty pounds.*
When do the servants go to bed?	*About ten o'clock.*
Where is Holmes now?	*I don't know.*

2 Complete the questions with the question words in the box. Use some question words more than once. Then match the questions with the answers 1–8.

> What   Where   Which   Who   Why

a .....*Why*..... do you need to see the bedrooms? ⑤
b .... window is your bedroom, Alec? ☐
c .... do the apples and water fall on the floor? ☐
d .... is the rest of the paper? ☐
e .... can we say about the paper? ☐
f .... is the writer? ☐
g .... does William's mother say about all this? ☐
h .... must we arrest these men? ☐

1 The handwriting is very strange.
2 Because Holmes hits the table with his foot.
3 It's the last window on the left.
4 Because they are the murderers.
5 Because I'd like to see the garden from there.
6 She knows nothing.
7 There are two writers, old Mr Cunningham and Alec Cunningham.
8 It is in the pocket of Alec's dressing gown.

GRAMMAR CHECK

Imperative verbs

We use imperatives to give instructions or order someone to do something.

We make the affirmative imperative with the infinitive without *to*.

Come with me!

We make the negative imperative with *don't* + the infinitive without *to*.

Don't go upstairs!

We often put please before an imperative verb, so the instruction or order is more polite or friendly.

Please sign this paper.   Please don't run away.

3 Complete the sentences with the imperatives in the box.

come̶ remember look come don't begin be open give

a Please ....*come*............ with me to the scene of the crime.

b Please .... working again.

c .... me half an hour with the inspector.

d .... the door, please.

e .... this: the thief takes nothing from our house.

f Hey, Watson, ... more careful!

g .... to the kitchen door at a quarter to twelve.

h .... carefully. The man with the stronger hand writes first.

4 Who or what says the sentences a–h in Activity 3? Match the sentences below with a–h from Activity 3.

1 Inspector Forrester says this to Sherlock Holmes. [a]

2 Holmes says this to a policeman next to the kitchen door. ☐

3 Dr Watson says this to his friend, Holmes. ☐

4 The letter to William Kirwan has these words. ☐

5 Holmes says this to Watson, Colonel Hayter, and Mr Acton. ☐

6 Holmes says this angrily to Watson. ☐

7 Alec Cunningham says this to Sherlock Holmes. ☐

8 Holmes says this to Watson, Hayter, and Acton. ☐

GRAMMAR CHECK

Present Simple: third person -s

We add -s to the infinitive without *to* to make the third person (*he/she/it*) form of the Present Simple.

Alec takes a pistol from his pocket. He gets ready to shoot.

When verbs end in -o, -ch, -ss, or -sh, we add -es to make the third person form.

watch – William watches the Cunninghams.

When verbs end in consonant + -y, we change the y to i and add -es .

cry – 'It's true,' the colonel cries.

The verbs have / have got and be are irregular.

We have (have got) the criminals and that's (that is) the important thing.

We can use the Present Simple to re-tell a story.

5 Put the verbs in brackets in the Present Simple and complete the text about the murder of William Kirwan.

Upstairs, in Alec Cunningham's bedroom, Holmes
a) .... *sees* .... (see) Alec's dressing gown on
the back of the door. In old Cunningham's room,
Holmes **b)** .... (hit) the table with the
apples and water. Everyone **c)** .... (come)
to help. Holmes **d)** .... (go) back to
Alec's room and **e)** .... (look) in the
pockets of the dressing gown. A piece of the
paper **f)** .... (be) there!

He **g)** .... (take) it, but the Cunninghams find him. Alec nearly **h)** .... (kill)
him. 'Help! Help! Murder!' Holmes **i)** .... (cry).
After the arrest, Holmes **j)** .... (talk) to old Cunningham. He **k)** .... (tell)
Holmes this: on the night of the crime at Acton's house, William Kirwan
l) .... (watch) the Cunninghams. He then **m)** .... (ask) them for money.
Alec **n)** .... (get) very angry and **o)** .... (want) to kill him. William
p) .... (get) the letter and that night, he **q)** .... (come) to the big house.
Alec **r)** .... (shoot) him. He **s)** .... (try) to take the letter from William,
but he **t)** .... (leave) some of it in William's hand.

GRAMMAR

GRAMMAR CHECK

Possessive forms

We use possessive adjectives to talk about possession.

Holmes goes to the country with his friend, Watson.

I	my
you	your
he/she/it	his/her/its
we	our
they	their

We use 's and ' to talk about possession with nouns and names.

We use 's with singular nouns and plural nouns without -s, and ' for most plural nouns.

Hayter – Hayter's house   the Cunninghams – the Cunninghams' house

We can use 's or ' for singular nouns and names ending in -s.

Holmes – Holmes's house is in Baker Street. ✔

Holmes – Holmes' house is in Baker Street. ✔

6 Complete these sentences with the correct possessive form.

a ......My...... friend Hayter wants me to visit him.

b .... house is in the country, near Reigate.

c Hayter.............. servant comes quickly into the room.

d The Cunninghams.............. servant, William Kirwan, is dead.

e What does.............. mother say about all of this?

f Finally, Holmes opens.............. eyes.

7 Match the parts of the sentences a–f with 1–6.

a Don't you have bars on …   **1** my father's bedroom.'

b The thief doesn't go upstairs. We know because we're in …   **2** your doors?

c Alec says, 'My bedroom is next to …   **3** 's bedroom.

d The cry comes from Alec …   **4** 's house

e Alec has his hands around Holmes …   **5** 's neck.

f They all go back to Colonel Hayter …   **6** our bedrooms.

49

GRAMMAR CHECK

Modal auxiliary verbs: can, can't, and must

We use *can* + infinitive without *to* to talk about things that we are able to do or that are possible.

Can you sign this paper, please? They can see the garden from the bedrooms.

We use *can't* + infinitive without *to* to talk about things that we are not able to do or that are not possible.

Holmes loves working – we can't stop him.

We use *must* + infinitive without *to* to talk about things that we have to do or that are an obligation.

Holmes is tired and ill. He must go home.

8 Choose the correct word to complete the sentences.

a Inspector Forrester *can* / *must* find the murderer. He wants Holmes's help.

b Mr Cunningham *can* / *must* see the man near the road.

c We have something important, a clue, and perhaps it *can* / *must* help us.

d Holmes is excited. We *can* / *can't* stop him. He loves working!

e William's mother *can* / *can't* tell us very much.

f Holmes *can* / *must* talk to the Cunninghams. They know the truth.

g He *can't* / *must* look in the pocket of the dressing gown.

h Please, *can* / *must* you look at the scene of the crime, Mr Holmes?

i Where *can* / *must* William be at a quarter to twelve?

j You *can* / *must* give me the money, or I'm going to the police.

k The inspector *can* / *can't* arrest the two criminals now.

l Now we have the criminals. We *can* / *must* go home to Baker Street tomorrow.

GRAMMAR

GRAMMAR CHECK

Prepositions and prepositional verbs

Prepositions of movement tell us where something is, or how and where something moves.

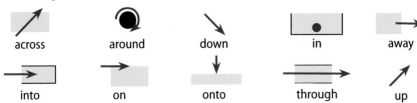

across   around   down   in   away

into   on   onto   through   up

Some verbs can take a preposition. You can understand many verbs with prepositions from the meaning of the separate words.

fall down   get up   run away

Some **verbs + prepositions** have a special meaning.

come on (= hurry)   look for (= try to find)

9 **Complete the sentences about *The Reigate Puzzle* with the prepositions in the box. Use some of the prepositions more than once.**

> across   around   down   from   in   into   on   onto   through   up

a They walk . . . . . . .through. . . . . . the trees to the Cunninghams' big old house.

b Watson is talking. Holmes looks . . . . from his chair.

c The murderer runs . . . . the garden.

d Then he runs away . . . . the hedge.

e Something terrible is happening to Holmes. He falls . . . . the ground.

f Alec Cunningham puts his big hands . . . . Holmes's neck.

g There's water near the hedge, so why are there no marks . . . . the ground?

h In the morning, at breakfast, Colonel Hayter's servant runs . . . . the room.

i Why are the thieves staying . . . . the village? Why don't they run
. . . . ?

j Alec takes a pistol . . . . his pocket and gets ready to shoot.

k Holmes quickly looks . . . . the pockets of Alec's dressing gown.

51

DOMINOES Your Choice

Read *Dominoes* for pleasure, or to develop language skills. It's your choice.

Each *Dominoes* reader includes:
- a good story to enjoy
- integrated activities to develop reading skills and increase vocabulary
- task-based projects – perfect for CEFR portfolios
- contextualized grammar activities.

Each *Dominoes* pack contains a reader and an excitingly dramatized audio recording of the story.

If you liked this *Domino*, read these:

Sherlock Holmes: The Speckled Band
Sir Arthur Conan Doyle

'Help me,' says Helen Stoner. 'My sister died, and now I am going to die too.' Sherlock Holmes and Dr Watson must answer the question of how Julia Stoner died, two years ago. If they cannot, then Helen Stoner will die too. But her house is very strange - and her stepfather, Dr Grimesby Roylott, is very angry and does not want Holmes there. Who killed Julia, and how? And why did she say 'The speckled band!' before she died?

The Great Fire of London
Janet Hardy-Gould

It's London, 1666. It's a hot, dry summer. A small fire starts in a baker's shop in Pudding Lane. Soon the city of London is burning and the fire-fighters can't stop the fire. People are running from their houses down to the River Thames.
But how does the fire begin and who can stop it? What is the King of England doing to help?

	CEFR	Cambridge Exams	IELTS	TOEFL iBT	TOEIC
Level 3	B1	PET	4.0	57-86	550
Level 2	A2–B1	KET-PET	3.0-4.0	–	390
Level 1	A1–A2	YLE Flyers/KET	3.0	–	225
Starter & Quick Starter	A1	YLE Movers	1.0–2.0	–	–

You can find details and a full list of books and teachers' resources on our website:
www.oup.com/elt/gradedreaders